D1586704

SOUTHWEST SCOTLAND

A LANDSCAPE FASHIONED BY GEOLOGY

©Scottish Natural Heritage 2008
ISBN 978 1 85397 520 2
A CIP record is held at the British Library
TC2.5K1108

Acknowledgements
Authors: Andrew McMillan (BGS) and Phil Stone (BGS)
Series editor: Alan McKirdy (SNH)

Photography: Alamy/Chuck Eckert 23 top; **Alamy/SW Images** 28; **Alamy/Vincent Lowe** 17; **Alan Devlin** 25 left; **Lorne Gill/SNH** front cover, frontispiece, 7, 8, 10, 13, 14, 14 inset, 16, 18, 19, 20, 24 top, 25 right, 29, 31, 33, 33 inset, 34, 36, 37; **John Gordon** 26; **BGS** 12, 21 top, 21 bottom left, 22, 32; **Patricia & Angus Macdonald/SNH** 5 top, 27 top; **Andrew McMillan** 30; **National Museums of Scotland** 9 top, 15, 35; **US Geological Survey** 6 top.

Illustrations: BGS 21 bottom right, 27 bottom; **Craig Ellery** 2, 3, 4, 5 bottom, 6 bottom, 11; **Clare Hewitt** 9 bottom, 24 bottom; **Ian McIntosh** contents; **Elizabeth Pickett/North Pennines AONB Partnership** 23 bottom.

Further copies of this book and other publications can be ordered online at **www.snh.org.uk/pubs**
or contact:
Publications,
Scottish Natural Heritage,
Battleby, Redgorton, Perth PH1 3EW
Tel: 01738 458530 Fax: 01738 458613
E-mail: pubs@snh.gov.uk

Front cover image:
View over Nithsdale
Back cover image:
The shore at Arbigland

SOUTHWEST SCOTLAND

A Landscape Fashioned by Geology

by

Andrew McMillan (BGS) and Phil Stone (BGS)

The main elements of the Southwest Scotland landscape

Contents

The southwest corner of Scotland rises from the coasts of the Solway Firth and Firth of Clyde into the broad rolling hills of the Southern Uplands. Five hundred million years of geological history are recorded in the rocks, which range from soft red sandstone to hard intractable granite. An ancient long-lost ocean, volcanoes, arid deserts, tropical forests, glaciers, the collision and splitting apart of huge continents; all of these phenomena have played their part in shaping the landscape, but the most profound was the relatively recent scouring by a vast ice sheet. Humans moved in as the glaciers retreated and have continued the modification, mining, quarrying, farming and building. The unique combination of all these influences has produced a wild and rugged mountainous core with an extensive periphery of arable land and pasture. Most of the main communication arteries run around that periphery, or up and over the main valleys and watersheds, but for the more intrepid the Southern Upland Way, a long-distance footpath, runs from west to east through the heart of the hills. Art and literary associations with the landscape are legion: the Impressionists such as The Glasgow Boys including E A Hornel, and the poets and authors including Sir Walter Scott, Robert Louis Stevenson, John Buchan, S R Crockett, Dorothy Sayers and, of course, Rabbie Burns - 'Ye banks and braes o' bonnie Doon, How can ye bloom sae fresh and fair?' Part of the answer lies in the geology.

Southwest Scotland Through Time

QUATERNARY
2.6 million years ago to the present day

Before 5,000 years ago. Human occupation began.
11,500 years ago. Vegetation started to recolonise the land with forests established by 5000 years ago.
12,500 to 11,500 years ago. Small corrie glaciers existed in the Galloway and Moffat hills.
15,000 to 12,500 years ago. Rapid deglaciation occurred as the climate warmed.
30,000 to 15,000 years ago. The last major ice sheets covered Galloway and the Southern Uplands.
Before 30,000 years ago. There were periods of very cold climate, and at times much of Britain was covered by ice-sheets. These periods were interspersed with warm (Interglacial) stages.

NEOGENE
23 to 2.6 million years ago

At about 2.6 million years ago, there was a dramatic cooling of the northern hemisphere, the beginning of the 'Ice Age'. Before that, tropical conditions existed. The south of Scotland is likely to have been a well-vegetated land mass at this time and was probably populated by a wide variety of herbivore animals including horses and hippos.

PALAEOGENE
65 to 23 million years ago

The youngest rocks in Southwest Scotland formed when masses of molten magma, sourced from the volcanoes of the Inner Hebrides, solidified in the earth's crust.

CRETACEOUS
145 to 65 million years ago

In western Scotland warm shallow seas existed, but the Galloway area is likely to have been dry land and no rocks of this period are preserved here.

JURASSIC
199 to 145 million years ago

Sea level changes meant that the fringes of Scotland were intermittently covered by shallow seas. No rocks of this period are preserved in Southwest Scotland but just to the south around Carlisle, there are Jurassic rocks with fossils of marine animals known as ammonites.

TRIASSIC
251 to 199 million years ago

Deposits of red sandstone and mudstone were laid down in rivers and ponds on a relatively flat desert plain. These rocks are found in eastern Dumfries-shire, where some of the mudstones contain early plant fossils.

PERMIAN
299 to 251 million years ago

Scotland lay just north of the equator. Deserts developed across most of southern Scotland and the red sandstones of Lochmaben, Thornhill, Dumfries and Stranraer show all the characteristics of desert dunes. Flash floods occurred from time to time. Fossil trackways in the sandstones preserve evidence of early reptiles.

CARBONIFEROUS
359 to 299 million years ago

Intermittent volcanic eruptions formed thin lava flows. Sedimentary rocks, now best seen along the Solway Coast, were laid down in a variety of settings including rivers, lakes and the sea. Abundant shells and coral fossils, and coals developed in swampy areas, all indicate a tropical equatorial climate.

DEVONIAN
416 to 359 million years ago

The Anglo-Scottish "join" was wrenched sideways allowing magma to rise up from great depth. Surface erosion took place in the arid Devonian environment and it is likely that the major valleys of Galloway began to develop at this time.

SILURIAN
444 to 416 million years ago

As the Iapetus Ocean closed thick layers of sand accumulated at the Scottish margin, but were folded and piled up into huge faulted slices as the ocean disappeared.

ORDOVICIAN
488 to 444 million years ago

The Iapetus Ocean began to close and volcanoes erupted at its margins. The volcanic rocks and thick layers of ocean-floor sediment were pushed onto the continental margin as huge faulted slices.

CAMBRIAN
542 to 488 million years ago

Scotland and England, then parts of different continents, were separated by the wide Iapetus Ocean. Scotland lay in the southern tropics; England was much farther south.

PRECAMBRIAN
Before 542 million years ago

Precambrian rocks formed within the continental masses that split apart to create the Iapetus Ocean, but no rocks formed at this time are preserved in Southwest Scotland.

Brown bars indicate periods of time represented by the rocks and loose sediments of Southwest Scotland.

Geological Map of Southwest Scotland

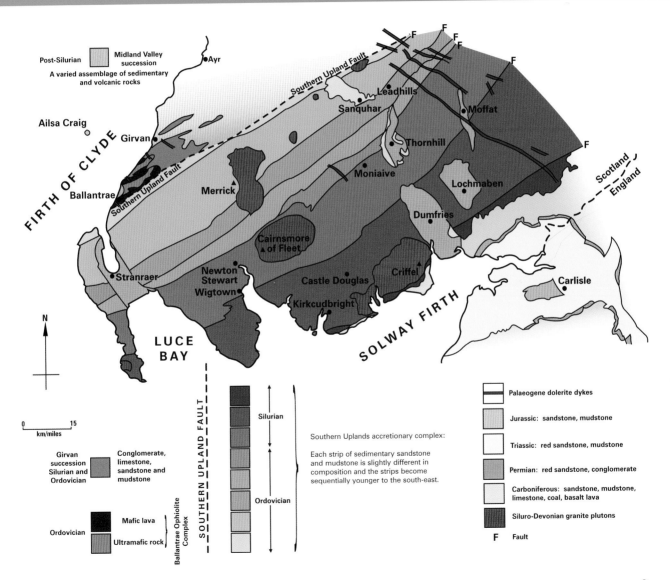

Post-Silurian   Midland Valley succession
A varied assemblage of sedimentary and volcanic rocks

FIRTH OF CLYDE

Ailsa Craig

•Ayr

Southern Upland Fault

•Leadhills
Sanquhar•
•Moffat

Girvan•

Ballantrae

Southern Upland Fault

•Thornhill

Merrick▲

•Moniaive

Lochmaben•

Cairnsmore
▲ of Fleet

•Dumfries

Scotland
England

F

Stranraer•

Newton
Stewart
Wigtown•

Castle Douglas•

•Criffel

•Carlisle

•Kirkcudbright

LUCE
BAY

SOLWAY FIRTH

N

0   15
km/miles

Girvan
succession
Silurian and
Ordovician

Conglomerate,
limestone,
sandstone and
mudstone

SOUTHERN UPLAND FAULT

Silurian

Ordovician

Southern Uplands accretionary complex:

Each strip of sedimentary sandstone
and mudstone is slightly different in
composition and the strips become
sequentially younger to the south-east.

Palaeogene dolerite dykes

Jurassic: sandstone, mudstone

Triassic: red sandstone, mudstone

Permian: red sandstone, conglomerate

Carboniferous: sandstone, mudstone,
limestone, coal, basalt lava

Siluro-Devonian granite plutons

F   Fault

Ordovician

Mafic lava

Ultramafic rock

Ballantrae Ophiolite Complex

The Iapetus Ocean

The Southern Uplands of Scotland lie immediately to the north of one of Britain's most fundamental geological divides. This is the so-called 'Iapetus Suture', the trace of an ancient ocean, Iapetus, which separated two continents and was destroyed by their slow convergence. To the north was Laurentia, of which Scotland formed a tiny part; to the south was Avalonia, containing embryonic England. The Iapetus Ocean was more than 1000 kilometres wide about 500 million years ago but then, along its margins, volcanic islands appeared as ocean crust was destroyed. The process had begun that, over the next 80 million years, would close the ocean. As shown in the sketch on page 6, the destruction of ocean crust as it sinks beneath the margin of a continent is called subduction. The opposite effect, when the ocean crust rides up on top of the continental margin, is called obduction. Incidentally, the name 'Iapetus' comes from Greek mythology. Iapetus was the father of Atlas - after whom the present-day Atlantic Ocean is named.

Early in the Ordovician Period, about 470 million years ago, the southern part of Scotland lay in the tropics, just to the south of the equator. Its surroundings would have looked a little like the western Pacific of today, with a complex pattern of active volcanic islands fringing the continental mainland. Away to the south stretched the Iapetus Ocean, with Avalonia (and England) forming its southern shores away down at a latitude of about 60° south. When the ocean eventually closed, about 420 million years ago, very different rocks and fossils were juxtaposed; their contrast provided one of the first clues to the reconfiguration of this ancient world.

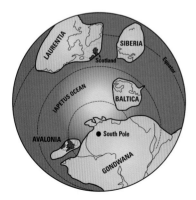

a. Late Cambrian circa 500 Million years ago

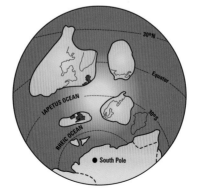

b. Late Ordovician circa 450 Million years ago

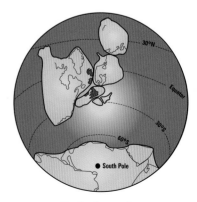

c. Early Devonian circa 400 Million years ago

View over Moffatdale towards the Grey Mare's Tail, White Coomb and Loch Skene

**d. Permian / Triassic
circa 250 Million years ago**

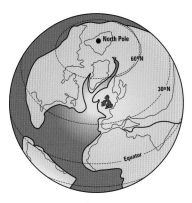

**e. Palaeogene
circa 50 Million years ago**

The closure of the Iapetus Ocean and subsequent plate collisions had, by 250 million years ago, combined all of the Earth's land masses into a single 'supercontinent', known as Pangaea. The subsequent break-up of Pangaea did not respect the earlier geological boundaries and the once-continuous margin of Laurentia is now divided by the still-spreading Atlantic Ocean. As a result the Early Palaeozoic rocks of southern Scotland have more in common with those of Newfoundland than with those of northern England, whilst the latter relate more closely to Nova Scotia than to Auld Scotland just to the north.

A Volcanic Collision - the Ballantrae Complex

Lava running into the sea, Hawaii

Between Girvan and Ballantrae, overlooking the Firth of Clyde, an unusual assemblage of rocks - the Ballantrae Complex - is testament to one phase in the destruction of the Iapetus Ocean about 480 million years ago. The complex was formed when volcanic islands escaped being subducted and were instead obducted, pushed up onto the margin of the Laurentian continent. In the process, distinctive rocks from 10 kilometres down beneath the seafloor were stacked up and mixed with lavas that had been erupted onto the sea floor. Such a relic of oceanic crust is generically known as an ophiolite complex, and the one at Ballantrae can be most readily interpreted when compared with the much bigger and better examples in places like Cyprus, Oman and Newfoundland.

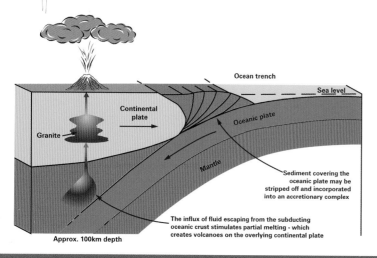

Ocean trench

Sea level

Continental plate

Oceanic plate

Granite

Mantle

Sediment covering the oceanic plate may be stripped off and incorporated into an accretionary complex

The influx of fluid escaping from the subducting oceanic crust stimulates partial melting - which creates volcanoes on the overlying continental plate

Approx. 100km depth

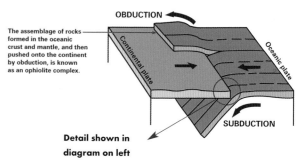

OBDUCTION

The assemblage of rocks formed in the oceanic crust and mantle, and then pushed onto the continent by obduction, is known as an ophiolite complex.

Continental plate

Oceanic plate

SUBDUCTION

Detail shown in diagram on left

Sketch showing the processes of subduction and obduction

Some of the rocks derived from great depth consist of minerals that are not very stable at the Earth's surface and so have been altered to 'serpentinite', so-called because of the sinuous patterns of red, green and brown that run through the rock and which were thought to be reminiscent of snake skin. Serpentinite is relatively soft and so has been readily eroded. It is only rarely exposed and at the coast tends to be buried beneath a raised beach backed by an old sea cliff cut in glacial deposits. Dykes and enclaves of harder, volcanic rock are left standing as sea stacks at the coast, for example at Lendalfoot, but further inland, around Colmonell, they have produced some spectacular crag and tail features in response to glacial erosion.

The volcanic lavas found at Ballantrae are commonly accumulations of pillow-shaped balls of basalt. This style is characteristic of submarine eruptions, where the lava is rapidly cooled by contact with seawater, and the resulting 'pillow-lavas' can be seen forming today around oceanic volcanoes like those of Hawaii. Many of the Ballantrae pillows were violently broken up by their rapid chilling so that thick beds made up of angular volcanic debris are interspersed amongst the lavas. The resulting massive volcanic sequence produces a rocky coastline and high sea cliffs at places such as Bennane Head; inland the volcanic rocks form the prominent hills such as Knockdolian.

The Early Ordovician age of the lavas in the Ballantrae Complex was established by fossils found in rare interbedded sedimentary rocks. Slightly younger, Late Ordovician pillow lavas occur just to the south of Ballantrae and their pillow structures are spectacularly developed. These lavas, at Downan Point, provide the finest examples of this volcanic feature to be seen in Britain.

A Subsiding Continental Margin - the Girvan Succession

Steeply dipping turbidite beds at Ardwell Bay, Ayrshire

The obduction of the ophiolite assemblage was a geologically brief event and soon the Ballantrae Complex and its continental foundation began to subside. Slowly the sea crept across the eroded remains of the ophiolite complex, which was progressively buried beneath sedimentary rocks deposited from the end of the Ordovician Period into the earliest Silurian.

Deposition of sediment was initially in shallow water encroaching onto the southern fringes of the ophiolite. Limestone reefs built up locally, and were home to a rich fauna of corals, shellfish, trilobites and other sea creatures; the calcareous alga *Girvanella* was abundant. The limestones inter-finger with thick beds of conglomerate, an accumulation of pebbles and boulders that originally poured

Above: Silurian trilobite

Below: Turbidity current in action and idealized turbidite sequence showing graded beds

across the subsiding continental margin in submarine fans derived from the land mass to the north. As subsidence continued, this shallow-water sedimentary assemblage edged northwards whilst, in the south, the older limestone and conglomerate beds sunk deeper and were buried by sandstone and mudstone, mostly deposited from underwater debris avalanches known as turbidity flows.

Turbidites - the deposits of turbidity flows - comprise myriad layers of sandstone and mudstone, mostly thin but with some beds of sandstone up to two metres thick and extending laterally for several kilometres. Each sandstone bed was deposited from a single, huge submarine flow of chaotically-mixed sediment. This slumped mass accelerated down the margin of the continent into the deeper water, but then slowed abruptly as it spread out across the sea floor. As the current slowed, its sediment load settled out; first the largest and heaviest particles, then progressively smaller and lighter grains. The result is a 'graded bed' with coarse grains of sand at its base and sequentially finer sand and silt appearing towards the top. Between successive turbidity flows only mud was deposited. This alternation produces the emphatically striped appearance of the rock succession seen on the coast south of Girvan.

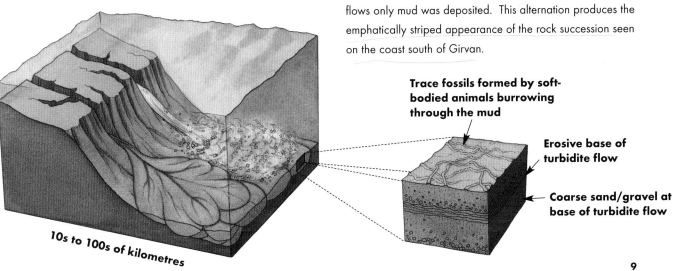

Trace fossils formed by soft-bodied animals burrowing through the mud

Erosive base of turbidite flow

Coarse sand/gravel at base of turbidite flow

10s to 100s of kilometres

A Tectonic Paradox - The Southern Uplands

Folded strata at Ardwell Bay, Wigtownshire

Whilst the late Ordovician seas were encroaching on the subsiding margin of the Laurentian continent, another sedimentary sequence was being deposited further south. Its history is now revealed by the rocks of the Southern Uplands, a geological massif that extends from the North Sea coast of Scotland south-westward into Northern Ireland, spanning the Dumfries and Galloway region. Across this wide expanse of rolling hills are seen tough, resistant sandstones. They record how, with the resumption of subduction, a deep ocean trench was established into which turbidity flows poured. A characteristic, banded succession of turbidite strata built up, but with important constraints on its development imposed by the highly active tectonic setting, similar to the environment seen today in the earthquake-prone trenches around Indonesia and Japan.

The Southern Uplands turbidite sandstones were deposited on top of the thin layer of muddy sediment that covered the ocean floor. But all the while the ocean floor was very slowly, at a rate of several centimetres per year, creeping towards destruction in the ocean trench subduction zone. So, once deposited, the turbidite sandstones were also carried on towards a similar fate. Instead of disappearing into oblivion, however, successive huge slices of sedimentary rock were stripped off the descending oceanic crust and stacked up, each new slice pushed in beneath those that had gone before. As the pile of rock slices got bigger, the original, nearly horizontal structures were steepened and now appear almost vertical. The major features seen today originated as the planes of movement, or faults, separating the sequentially incorporated slices.

Diagram showing the formation of the Southern Uplands sandstone succession.

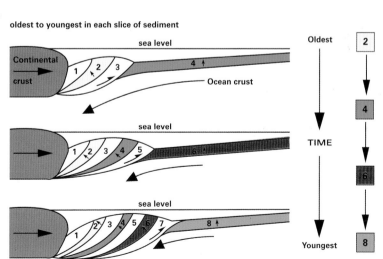

As the ocean crust descends beneath the continental margin, sequentially younger layers of sediment are scraped off and incorporated at the bottom of a pile of similar, but older slices.

Steeply dipping and inclined turbidite sandstones at Brighouse Bay

The faults now form more readily eroded lines of weakness that run northeast to southwest and determine the orientation of major valleys such as Glen App and Moffatdale. The faults separate tracts of steeply inclined turbidite beds that also run northeast to southwest across the country.

The turbidite deposits dominate the succession so that between any two major faults, thousands of metres of sandstone beds may overlie only a few metres of the ocean floor mudstone, with the succession getting younger towards the northwest. But the stacking up of rock slices has produced paradoxical stratigraphical relationships, and fossils show that overall the rocks become younger towards the southeast. This is the result of the sequential incorporation of successively younger sediment slices beneath previously incorporated slices. Since deformation of the sandstone turbidite beds largely occurred as they were incorporated, the folds produced - and there are lots of them - are also older in the north than in the south.

View southwest along the fault line from above the Grey Mare's Tail car-park, Moffatdale

Graptolites – Celebrity Fossils

At first sight, the seemingly vast and intractable turbidite succession of the Southern Uplands of Scotland must have presented a daunting geological challenge. The key that unlocked its secrets was a group of humble fossils called graptolites, the remains of small, free-floating colonies of marine organisms. Through the late Ordovician and the Silurian Periods graptolites were evolving rapidly and so different assemblages of them can be used to date the rocks; at best, graptolites can be used to identify divisions representing the sedimentary accumulation of less than half a million years.

Dob's Linn in Moffatdale is a gash in the hillside where a waterfall cascades down the vertical base of a massive turbidite sandstone bed and into a stream that tumbles through a gorge cut into the underlying oceanic mudstone. Here, a pioneering study of graptolites was carried out during the 1870s by Charles Lapworth, then a schoolmaster in Galashiels but later to become Professor of Geology at the University of Birmingham. Dob's Linn was a pivotal location

in his investigation, for in this stream section he was able to establish a complete, unbroken succession of graptolitic mudstone spanning the Late Ordovician and the Early Silurian Periods. This provided the key to age relationships across the whole region. Crucially, it was used by the Victorian geologists Ben Peach and John Horne, who applied Lapworth's scheme during their mapping of the Southern Uplands for the Geological Survey between 1880 and 1890. The sequence of graptolite 'biozones' worked out in those early days has stood the test of time and is still broadly applicable today.

The importance of the Dob's Linn site has also carried forward into modern times with its formal adoption by the international geological community as the global standard used to define the beginning of the Silurian Period. This would undoubtedly have astonished Halbert Dobson, the 17th century Covenanter who hid from Government Dragoons in a cave above the waterfall at Dob's Linn, and after whom it is named.

Continents Meet - Faults, Folds and Granite

View northwest over farmland looking towards Cairnsmore of Fleet NNR

Sometime late in the Silurian Period, round about 425 million years ago, the last remnants of the Iapetus Ocean were subducted and Laurentia collided with Avalonia. We might expect this to have been a dramatic event, with intense deformation and the rise of a mountain range, rather as the collision of India and Asia has thrown up the Himalayas. But as far as the rocks of Southwest Scotland were concerned, continental collision was a bit of an anticlimax. There was no major deformation and instead the Southern Uplands stack of turbidite slices, at the leading edge of Laurentia, initially

rode up onto and pushed down the margin of the Avalonian continent. In this first meeting of Scotland and England it seems that Scotland came out on top.

The deformation that was preserved in the rocks shows that for part of the time the two continents slid past each other rather than towards each other. Within the Southern Uplands, accommodating movement was concentrated into the weaker zones, mainly along the pre-existing faults in the near-vertical mudstone sequence at the base of the

Merrick, highest hill in the Southern Uplands, and Loch Valley, seen from the Rig of The Jarkness

sandstone-dominated tracts, but locally the sandstones were folded as well. In some places, wider zones of more pervasive deformation were developed: the best example of the latter runs southwest from Moniaive and is several kilometres across at its widest point.

But perhaps the most important result of the continental collision was that it upset the balance of forces deep in the Earth's crust and as a result, about 400 million years ago, triggered the rise of molten magma. Some of this was injected upwards into vertical cracks where it solidified into sheets known as dykes. The dykes commonly occur in swarms, where many crowd together in close proximity; they may have fed erupting volcanoes that have been completely eroded away, or they may never have reached the Earth's surface. Elsewhere, the magma rose in much larger masses before cooling and solidifying deep underground to form granite plutons. The latter have been a major influence on the landscape of Southwest Scotland, their eroded remains forming the high, rounded hills of Criffel and Cairnsmore of Fleet. Farther north, the effect of the granite has been more subtle. Some of the hills to the south of Loch Doon, such as Mullwharchar, are indeed of granite, but the highest mountain, Merrick (843 metres), and the equally rugged Rhinns of Kells lie just outside the granite outcrop. There, the intruding hot granite has baked and hardened the surrounding sandstone to such an extent that the latter is now the more resistant to weathering and erosion.

Volcanoes, Rivers and a Tropical Sea

Basalt lavas under Skippers Bridge, Langholm

From about 360 million years ago, at the beginning of the Carboniferous Period, the sedimentary rocks of the south of Scotland were deposited in rivers and shallow seas that intermittently encroached onto the land. The south of Scotland was then situated near the Equator and enjoyed a tropical climate! The area around today's Solway Firth was a subsiding centre of sediment deposition (known as the Solway Basin). Good exposures of the sedimentary rocks including sandstones, mudstones and limestones can be seen around Langholm in the River Esk and Liddel Water, and along the coast at Southerness.

Early in the Carboniferous, sediment deposition was interrupted by a volcanic episode, during which thin lava flows of the Birrenswark Lavas were erupted from fissures cut in the Earth's surface just like those of modern Iceland. Today's landscape shows these basalt flows occupying both the hill tops north of Ecclefechan and river beds (e.g. in the River Esk below Skipper's Bridge south of Langholm).

The volcanic rocks are overlain by thick white sandstones, which formed as sands filling the channels of large rivers that flowed southwards. At Whita Hill, near Langholm, these sandstones were easily exploited during the past 150 years as a source of good building stone for local towns and villages.

Faults and Fossils

Higher in the Carboniferous sequence, successions of sediments were laid down alternately in shallow seas and in rivers, in response to changes in sea level. These global changes were controlled by the melting and freezing of massive polar ice sheets. Along the Southerness to Arbigland shore of the Solway and in the Liddel Water at Penton Linns, east of Canonbie, shells and coral fossils together with the traces of burrowing worms indicate that these sediments were laid down in shallow tropical seas.

The present coast northeast of Southerness shows folded and deformed strata, including thick beds of sandstone and interbedded fossil-bearing mudstones and siltstones and occasional algal beds. At Thirlstane, a 15 metres thick sandstone bed now favoured by rock climbers shows evidence of earthquake activity, the soft beds of unconsolidated sand having once been disrupted due to the ground shaking. These sediments were deposited near to the line of a major fault or tear in the Earth's crust known as the North Solway Fault. The Fault is best seen from the viewpoint at Castlehill Point, Rockcliffe.

Inland, Carboniferous sedimentary rocks are seen at
Thornhill and Sanquhar. At Closeburn and Barjarg
thick limestones were worked in quarries and shallow
mines during the late 18th century as a source of lime
for agricultural purposes. One of the local farmers who
used Closeburn lime was the poet Rabbie Burns, who
farmed for a time at Ellisland. The limestones yielded
some spectacular marine fossil shells, including large
nautiloids (the precursor of the modern octopus and
squid). Some of these fossils may be seen in the
National Museum of Scotland, Edinburgh.

1cm

**Fossil nautilus found
at Closeburn**

A coral from Arbigland Bay

1cm

**Artist's impression of a
Carboniferous tropical sea with
marine creatures now
preserved as fossils**

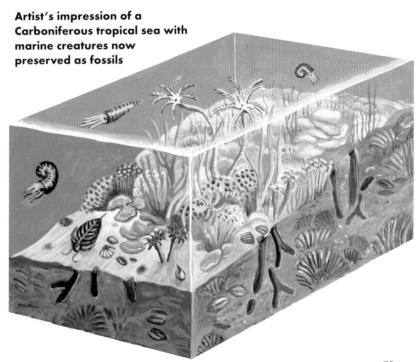

Coal and Swamps

During the late Carboniferous, shallow seaways occupied valleys through the Southern Uplands between the Solway and the Midland Valley. Coal Measures sediments were laid down in swamps and estuaries in a steamy tropical climate. Some speculate that all of the Southern Uplands were once covered by Coal Measures sedimentary rocks. Whether or not this was the case, all we see in this area today are remnants at Langholm, Thornhill, Sanqhuar and Stranraer. Typically, cyclical sequences (or measures) of seatrock, coal, mudstone and sandstone were deposited in subsiding swamps and the sequences of rocks represent the changing conditions with time. At the base of each sequence, seatrocks are made up of the fossilised roots of the tropical trees growing in swampy conditions. A modern analogy is a mangrove swamp in Florida. Above the rooty beds, coal developed from a mass of vegetation compressed by the weight of overlying sediments. These overlying strata included mudstones, often packed with freshwater mussel fossils which indicate the development of lakes across the swamp. At the top of the sequence, sandstones were deposited in river channels. Occasionally subsidence was so rapid that the sea encroached across the land resulting in the formation of limestones above the river sediments. Then the cycle of rocks began all over again.

Thus the Coal Measures contains many seams of coal and it was these that were exploited in many parts of Britain, including locally at Sanquhar and Cumnock where coals were worked underground until the 1970s and latterly in opencast pits. Coal seams are also present in the concealed coalfield south of Canonbie where deep mining finished in the 1920s.

5cm

Fossil mussel shells found in the Coal Measures

Present day swamp, Florida

Reconstruction of the shallow
rivers and swampy environment of
coal formation

Volcanoes in the Desert... then the Atlantic Opens

Detail cut in red sandstone, Sweetheart Abbey

Above the Coal Measures at Thornhill is a thin development of volcanic basaltic rocks. This outpouring of lavas on the uplifted land surface heralded the beginning of the Permian Period (about 300 million years ago), a time of desert conditions during which thick sequences of red sandstones formed from the accumulation of desert sand dunes. Occasional flash floods transported boulders and rock fragments across the desert plains and these accumulated to form conglomerates. These red beds are now found in several discrete areas, at Thornhill, Lochmaben, Dumfries and Stranraer, in successions locally more than 1500 metres thick. The red sandstones have proved to be excellent sources of building stone which has been used in Dumfries and exported for use in many UK towns and cities and overseas. They also form the most important aquifers in the south of Scotland and groundwater has been abstracted from these rocks, both for domestic and industrial uses, especially around Dumfries.

By Triassic time, starting about 250 million years ago, broad, shallow rivers meandered across an arid landscape. Few plants grew on this surface and the red soils were often exposed. Purple and grey mudstones and red sandstones laid down in the rivers underlie a large tract of land east of Annan. The rocks contain sedimentary structures such as ripple surfaces, rain drop imprints and sand-filled desiccation cracks indicating that from time to time these desert rivers and ponds dried up. The red sandstones known as the St Bees Sandstone (after St Bees Head in Cumbria) also provided good quality building sandstone, as can be seen in the towns and villages of northern Cumbria and eastern Dumfries. Much stone was exported to the USA and Canada, via ports such as Silloth in Cumbria, as ballast to supplement North American supplies of 'Brownstone.' Sandstones from Southwest Scotland can be seen today in New York and Boston.

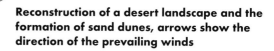

Reconstruction of a desert landscape and the formation of sand dunes, arrows show the direction of the prevailing winds

Looking towards Ailsa Craig from Ballantrae

Any younger sedimentary rocks that might once have covered Southwest Scotland have long since been eroded away. Some igneous rocks of Palaeogene age (65 million years ago) have survived, vestiges of the massive volcanic activity that accompanied the opening of the Atlantic Ocean. Most impressive is Ailsa Craig, a precipitous island off Girvan formed from a plug of granitic rock with an unusual composition, distinctive appearance and uniform hardness that makes it a great favourite for curling stones. Dykes of similar age can also be found, cutting across the older rocks. The most extensive, such as the Cleveland and Eskdalemuir dykes, though only a few metres across, can be traced all the way from northern England back to an ancient volcano on Mull.

The Ice Age

South Patagonian Icefield

Across the northern hemisphere rapid changes in climate occurred at the beginning of the Quaternary, some 2.6 million years ago. Alternating phases of warm climate were interspersed with colder periods. Some 750,000 years ago most of Britain was subjected to a prolonged glaciation known as the Anglian Glaciation. At this time the south of Scotland may have been completely covered by an ice sheet although there is little direct evidence for this. The most recent glaciation, the Late Devensian Glaciation, took place some 20,000 years ago, as determined by evidence from cores through the Greenland ice sheet. Again, during the maximum stages of the glaciation much of the Southern Uplands was probably overtopped by ice. From about 15,000 years ago, the climate warmed and the ice sheet melted, glaciers occupied the steep-sided valleys, and large volumes of sediment were transported downstream by meltwater. By about 12,500 years ago, all the glaciers had disappeared but then, for a short period of about 1000 years, small corrie glaciers reappeared in the Galloway mountains and Moffat Hills.

Blanket forestry and the glacially scoured Devil's Beeftub, near Moffat

The cycle of climatic change has left a marked signature on the present-day landscape. Both erosional and depositional processes of the ice sheets and the weathering of bedrock during warm inter-glacial interludes can be detected in upland areas. On the low ground in the valleys, thick accumulations of glacial debris developed in the form of till, a compact clay full of a jumble of ice-smoothed pebbles and boulders. Across Wigtownshire and Kirkcudbrightshire, both till deposits and exposed bedrock were moulded into well-formed drumlins, elongated mounds with sharp crests which were aligned in the direction of ice flow.

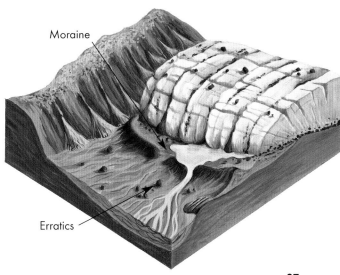

Moraine

Erratics

27

Upland Glaciers

Erratic granite boulders on the Devil's Bowling Green near Craignaw in Galloway Forest Park

Evidence of the glaciers is abundant. Glaciers had the effect of overdeepening pre-existing valleys, some of which show a 'U'-shaped profile. In some upland areas near the heads of valleys in the Galloway mountains and in the hills above Moffat, moundy accumulations of gravelly debris termed 'moraine' were formed at times when the snout of the glacier remained stationary for short periods of time during general retreat.

In areas underlain by granite, such as around Loch Doon, large granite boulders that were picked up and moved short distances by ice now perch directly on bare rock. Other granite boulders have been transported by ice well beyond the area of granite outcrop and abandoned as spectacular erratic blocks, the term 'erratic' meaning not of local origin. The power to transport material by major ice streams is demonstrated by the present distribution of granite erratics from Criffel and Ailsa Craig, which have travelled the length of the Irish Sea and across northern England.

In upland areas today, the steep slopes of mountain valleys are partly clothed in turf and heather and partly exhibit bare craggy rock surfaces and associated screes. Scree formation probably began at the earliest stages of deglaciation, some 15,000 years ago, and continued to occur at intervals. Piles of gravel and boulders accumulated at the foot of gullies or tributary streams to major valleys forming evocative fan-shaped deposits imprinted on the valley floor landscape. Around 5000 years ago, the landscape was covered in trees, a mixture of deciduous and pine, but with human settlement and the use of wood for fuel and construction, this canopy was removed. Recent studies of alluvial fans emanating from the steep slopes indicate that with clearance of forests and the introduction of agriculture to upland areas from about 3000 years ago, extensive hillslope gullying took place. Attempts to re-create wooded glens such as at Carrifran Glen in Moffatdale have been supported by communities and heritage agencies.

The Glacial Lowlands

The valley floors of the major rivers (Cree, Dee, Annan, Nith) are characterised by mounds and ridges of meltwater gravels which accumulated as valley glaciers melted and receded over many seasons. Many of the valley floors today contain small 'misfit' rivers within broad corridors of flat floodplains and higher river terraces, some of which formed as the glaciers receded. These modern rivers would have been dwarfed by the huge torrents of meltwater which flooded the same valleys, as the glaciers started to melt. Glacier ice melted seasonally so there were winter periods of little sedimentation followed by spring and summer influxes of sand and gravel.

From about 14,000 years ago, melting glaciers across the northern hemisphere led to a rise in global sea level. However, along coastal areas of the Solway, the early onset of this was relatively slow as sea level interacted with the general (isostatic) rise of the land as the weight of the ice was removed. The land continued to rise long after the change in sea level and this has resulted in beaches and marine deposits being lifted high and dry. Remnants of these raised beaches now preserve isolated pockets of sands and gravels up to 20 metres above present sea level. Raised beach gravels, deposited about 7,000 years ago, are well preserved south of Girvan. Here they lie on a prominent wave-cut platform, with rocky sea stacks, about 5 metres above present-day sea level.

In estuarine areas, beach barriers sometimes blocked access to the sea as the land continued to rise. Some of the best examples can be seen south of Dumfries where thick peat deposits started to accumulate, protected from invasion by the sea by shingle barriers. The Solway lowlands are home to a variety of migratory birds, for example the raised tidal flats of the Caerlaverock wetlands are visited each autumn by about 25,000 barnacle geese.

View over Nithsdale

Man Arrives on the Scene

As the ice sheets finally retreated, early Man spread into Southwest Scotland. Evidence for Mesolithic occupations is tantalisingly sparse and restricted to a few sites but by Neolithic times, about 5000 years ago, the area was well populated. Dating from then, and the succeeding Bronze Age, are chambered cairns, cup and ring carvings, stone circles and individual standing stones, which have a particular concentration in the Whithorn peninsula - The Machars. The town of Whithorn was also a centre of early Christianity, founded by St Ninian in 397 AD, with the local Silurian sandstone utilized for carved religious monuments across a wider area of Galloway from the 5th century onwards.

Local building stone was used in defensive Iron Age earthworks but its acquisition became more organised as larger quantities were required for medieval castles. The impressively cliff-edged Dunskey Castle, south of Portpatrick, is typical in being constructed largely of Southern Uplands turbidite sandstone but with dressed corner stones and lintels of the much softer Permian red sandstone, most probably sourced in the Dumfries area. By that time the quarrying of the readily worked Permian sandstone must have been well established, since it was used extensively from 1273 onwards in the building of Sweetheart Abbey. This Cistercian establishment to the south of Dumfries, now a picturesque ruin, was founded by Devorgilla, Lady of Galloway, in memory of her husband John Balliol.

The Permian red sandstone has proved a popular building stone, both in the UK and overseas, and its extraction continues today at Locharbriggs Quarry, to the north of Dumfries. The Galloway granites have also been quarried, particularly the Criffel intrusion whose coastal location made transport of the extracted stone a little easier. The largest quarries were near Dalbeattie where granite setts were traditionally the primary product. Building and dimension stone was also won and was much used in Dalbeattie and Castle Douglas. Large quantities of the Galloway granites were also shipped to Liverpool for construction of the Docks. Hard rock aggregate is currently produced from quarries at Dalbeattie and Creetown.

Splitting a granite block at
Silver Grey Quarries, Creetown, around 1939
Inset right: Stone circle at Torhousemuir near Wigtown

Mineral Treasures

In two areas of Southwest Scotland, geological processes have conspired to concentrate metallic minerals into veins and so allowed development of mainly 18th and 19th century mining industries. Most important was the Leadhills-Wanlockhead district which, between 1700 and 1958, produced 400 000 tonnes of lead, 10,000 tonnes of zinc and 25 tonnes of silver; in addition, the area's stream sediments were an important source of gold. Farther west, mining of copper, lead and zinc ores in Galloway was more dispersed: near Carsphairn, between Newton Stewart and Gatehouse of Fleet, and around Dalbeattie. From a site in the last of these areas intermittent production of baryte (barium sulphate, then used mainly in paint manufacture) continued until 1954, but elsewhere in Galloway mining had ceased by 1920.

Most of the mineral veins were probably formed during the Carboniferous Period. Metal sulphides such as galena (lead), sphalerite (zinc) and chalcopyrite (copper) were the main ore minerals, although in the Leadhills-Wanlockhead mines a great range of unusual secondary minerals were also encountered. Hence we have Leadhillite and Susannite, each of which is a mixed sulphate-carbonate of lead; the latter is named after the Susannah Vein, the source of the former name is more obvious as is that of Caledonite, a complex copper-lead mineral. Other unusual secondary minerals have been created in the spoil heaps by the weathering and alteration of discarded ore.

The alluvial gold in the Leadhills-Wanlockhead area has been of particular historical significance. It was discovered at Crawford Muir in the early 16th century and by 1542 was being used in significant quantities for royal crowns and jewellery and in the minting of coins. Production declined as the richest deposits were worked out but intermittent sluicing operations continued until relatively recently, and gold can still be panned today from many of the local streams. Although there are reports of gold-bearing quartz veins having been discovered, the bedrock source of the gold remains completely unknown. Modern microchemical investigations suggest that it might even be derived from a number of different sources.

Mining tends to leave its mark on the landscape long after activity has ceased, but in both of the old mining districts there is an increasing interest in industrial archaeology and the preservation of the surviving heritage. Wanlockhead is now the site for Scotland's Museum of Lead Mining, and includes an underground drift working restored for public access. Less of the mining infrastructure survives in Galloway, but at several sites the remains of mine buildings, shafts and crushing floors can still be seen.

Caledonite crystals

The Landscape Today - Rocks, Wind and Rain

The old railway viaduct at Gatehouse of Fleet

Port Logan Botanical Garden

There is a lot of rain - an average of up to about 1275 millemetres per annum with more over the mountains. Not surprising then that the region was a pioneer in hydro-electricity generation, with the Galloway scheme based on Loch Ken initiated in 1929. Clatteringshaws Loch was greatly expanded as part of this enterprise, with a large quarry opened in the adjacent Cairnsmore of Fleet granite to provide material for the dam. More recently, energy generation has switched to wind power, with wind farms appearing, sometimes controversially, in the exposed upland areas.

Transport links across the region have always been dictated by the landscape, itself influenced by the underlying rocks. The principal east-west route follows the low-lying coastal fringe along the north shore of the Solway Firth. Though the railway is long-abandoned, its circuitous route is still picked out by the viaducts made famous by John Buchan in The Thirty-Nine Steps. The main north-south route rises over the watershed between the catchments of the rivers Annan and Clyde and recently has been radically developed with the construction of the M74 motorway. Large roadside cuttings now expose swathes of the Southern Uplands' sandstone and mudstone that Charles Lapworth puzzled over in obscure stream sections only 130 years ago.

The coastal fringe of Dumfries and Galloway enjoys a relatively mild climate thanks to the balmy influence of the Gulf Stream ocean current. As a result, the Port Logan Botanical Garden at the southern end of the Rhins of Galloway boasts a fine collection of palms and tree ferns. The more exposed and rocky upland areas, with only a thin covering of poor-quality, acidic soil, support more robust trees - the spruce and pine of commercial forestry which has expanded dramatically since the 1940s. For at least two centuries blackface sheep were a common sight across the rough uplands, supporting the livelihoods of many Galloway farms. Across the lowland areas, the blanket of glacial sediments gives rise to better soils and supports pastureland for sheep and cattle, with the distinctive black and white Belted Galloway cows a much-loved feature of the landscape.

Scottish Natural Heritage
and the British Geological Survey

Scottish Natural Heritage is a government body. Its aim is to help people enjoy Scotland's natural heritage responsibly, understand it more fully and use it wisely so that it can be sustained for future generations.

Scottish Natural Heritage
Great Glen House,
Leachkin Road
Inverness IV3 8NW

The British Geological Survey maintains up-to-date knowledge of the geology of the UK and its continental shelf. It carries out surveys and geological research.
The Scottish Office of BGS is sited in Edinburgh. The office runs an advisory and information service, a geological library and a well-stocked geological bookshop.

British Geological Survey
Murchison House
West Mains Road
Edinburgh EH9 3LA

British Geological Survey
NATURAL ENVIRONMENT RESEARCH COUNCIL

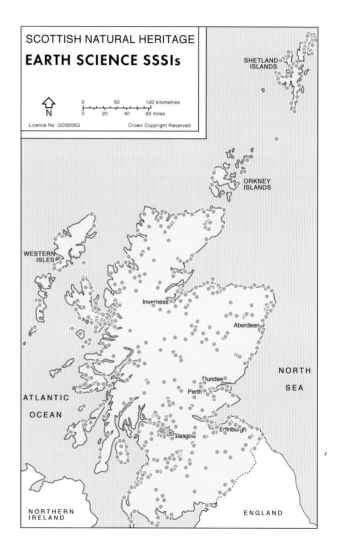

SCOTTISH NATURAL HERITAGE
EARTH SCIENCE SSSIs

N

0   50   100 kilometres
0   20   40   60 miles

Licence No. GD3006G   Crown Copyright Reserved

SHETLAND ISLANDS

ORKNEY ISLANDS

WESTERN ISLES

Inverness

Aberdeen

ATLANTIC OCEAN

Dundee

Perth

NORTH SEA

Glasgow   Edinburgh

NORTHERN IRELAND

ENGLAND

Remember the
Geological Code!

SCOTTISH NATURAL HERITAGE

GEOLOGISTS' ASSOCIATION 1858

No need to hammer indiscriminately! Never collect from walls or buildings.

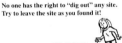

Keep collecting to a minimum: remove fossils, rocks or minerals only when essential for serious study. And remember to refer good finds to local museums.

The leader of a field party should ensure that the spirit of the code is upheld.

Always seek permission before entering private land.

No one has the right to "dig out" any site. Try to leave the site as you found it!

Don't litter fields or roads with rock fragments, and avoid disturbing plants or wildlife.

Back fill excavations where necessary to avoid injury to people or animals.

Be considerate, and do not make things more difficult or hazardous for others coming after you.

Don't disfigure rock surfaces with brightly painted numbers, symbols or clusters of core-holes.

- Remember, you are one of several hundred geologists visiting this area every year — so your behaviour *does* matter.
- Please observe the code, so that others can also enjoy the great scenery, geology, and ecology here!

SAFETY FIRST!
✔ Wear protective goggles when hammering.
✔ Wear safety hats in quarries or below cliffs.
✔ Avoid loosening rocks on steep slopes.
✗ Do not get cut off by the tide.
✗ Do not enter old mine workings or cave systems.
✗ Do not interfere with machinery in quarries.

Published by Scottish Natural Heritage, 1996.

Ben Nevis and Glencoe
Kathryn Goodenough & David Stephenson
ISBN 1 85397 506 6 pbk 44pp £4.95

Cairngorms
John Gordon, Rachel Wignall, Ness Brazier,
and Patricia Bruneau
ISBN 1 85397 455 2 pbk 52pp £4.95

Edinburgh and West Lothian
David McAdam
ISBN 1 85397 327 0 pbk 44pp £4.95

Fife and Tayside
Mike Browne, Alan McKirdy & David McAdam
ISBN 1 85397 110 3 pbk 36pp £3.95

Glen Roy
Douglas Peacock, John Gordon & Frank May
ISBN 1 85397 360 2 pbk 36pp £4.95

Loch Lomond to Stirling
Mike Browne & John Mendum
ISBN 1 85397 119 7 pbk 26pp £2.00

Mull and Iona
David Stephenson
ISBN 1 85397 423 4 pbk 44pp £4.95

Northwest Highlands
John Mendum, Jon Merritt & Alan McKirdy
ISBN 1 85397 139 1 pbk 52pp £6.95

Orkney and Shetland
Clive Auton, Terry Fletcher & David Gould
ISBN 1 85397 220 7 pbk 24pp £2.50

The Outer Hebrides
Kathryn Goodenough & Jon Merritt
ISBN 1 978185397 507 3 pbk ??pp £4.95

Rum and the Small Isles
Kathryn Goodenough & Tom Bradwell
ISBN 1 85397 370 2 pbk 48pp £5.95

Skye
David Stephenson & Jon Merritt
ISBN 1 85397 026 3 pbk 24pp £3.95

Scotland: the creation of its natural landscape
Alan McKirdy & Roger Crofts
ISBN 1 85397 004 2 pbk 64pp £7.50

Series Editor: Alan McKirdy (SNH)
Other books soon to be produced in the series
include: Argyll & the Islands, Moray & Caithness

SNH Publication Order Form

Title	Price	Quantity
Ben Nevis and Glencoe	£4.95	
Cairngorms	£4.95	
Edinburgh and West Lothian	£4.95	
Fife and Tayside	£3.95	
Glen Roy	£4.95	
Loch Lomond to Stirling	£2.00	
Mull and Iona	£4.95	
Northwest Highlands	£6.95	
Orkney and Shetland	£2.50	
The Outer Hebrides	£4.95	
Rum and the Small Isles	£5.95	
Southwest Scotland	£4.95	
Skye	£3.95	
Scotland: the Creation of its Natural Landscape	£7.50	

Postage and packing: free of charge in the UK, a standard charge of £2.95 will be applied to all orders from the European Union. Elsewhere a standard charge of £5.50 will be applied for postage.

TOTAL

Please complete in **BLOCK CAPITALS**

Name

Address

Post Code

Method   ☐ Mastercard   ☐ Visa   ☐ Switch   ☐ Solo   ☐ Cheque

Name of card holder

Card Number

☐☐☐☐ ☐☐☐☐ ☐☐☐☐ ☐☐☐☐

Valid from ☐☐ ☐☐   Expiry Date ☐☐ ☐☐

Issue no. ☐☐   Security Code ☐☐☐
(last 3 digits on reverse of card)

Send order and cheque made payable to Scottish Natural Heritage to:
Scottish Natural Heritage, Design and Publications, Battleby, Redgorton, Perth PH1 3EW Tel: 01738 458530

pubs@snh.gov.uk **or order online at: www.snh.org.uk/pubs**